# FUN to LEARN
# Science

## Graham Peacock
## Illustrated by Clare Beaton

## Educational Advisory Panel

Bernard Ashley – Head teacher and author

Diana Bentley – Language adviser

Peter Patilla – Lecturer and author

Susie Sainsbury – Nursery teacher

WALKER BOOKS
AND SUBSIDIARIES
LONDON · BOSTON · SYDNEY · AUCKLAND

Notes to Parents

Science is all around you: this series of books encourages children to look around and observe how things work in the pattern of normal life. Each page offers an activity that can be carried out from the illustration with a minimum of equipment. To children, each one is fun to do and to share; for parents there is the reassuring knowledge that the activities are worthwhile and that they reinforce the children's work at school.

In order to help your children:
* talk through the activities and listen well to their responses
* encourage them to talk about the pictures as much as the science involved
* talk about different approaches to each question, rather than imposing one method of working
* praise them frequently
* don't do too much in one session, but let them return to the pages they enjoy most

Notes on the educational purpose of each topic are listed below, with a reference in brackets to the specific subject area covered.

1 **Odd one out**
(The variety of life)
These pages introduce ideas about living things as plants or animals. You could also play the odd-one-out game with actual objects. In the kitchen you could use fruit and vegetables, for instance.

2 **Living things**
(The variety of life)
Develops discussion on living things. The definition of living is that things can grow and reproduce. The difference between plants and animals is that plants get their food from sunlight, while animals must eat plants or other animals. You could of course add people as a further form of a living animal.

3 **Where flowers grow**
(Processes of life)
On this page the main idea is to recognize that many plants need flowers for reproduction. Flowers are found on small plants and on trees.

4 **From bud to seed**
(Processes of life)
Extending the stage of plant reproduction from the previous page. Following the cycle of flowers, fruit and seeds.

**5  Different kinds of fruit**
(Processes of life)
Fruits come in all shapes, all fruits being the bearers of seeds. All the fruits on the right are citrus fruits.

**6  Natural collections**
(Earth and atmosphere)
Identification is not important here, but the names are listed at the end.

**7  Litter collection**
(Human influences on the Earth)
People produce waste products which sometimes become litter. Look at the difference between natural bio-degradable litter and other litter. Talk about where most litter collects in your neighbourhood. How could litter be prevented?

**8  Hard and soft**
(Types and uses of materials)
A simple activity which will encourage children to explore and describe the properties of everyday objects. Try sorting piles of hard and soft objects at home.

**9  Materials**
(Types and uses of materials)
An introduction to different materials. Encourage children to handle things and guess what they are made of.

**10  Windy day**
(Earth and atmosphere)
Light objects such as litter and hats are moved easily by the wind. The kite, yacht and windsurfer will only work when there is wind. Wind helps the washing to dry.

**11  Moving air**
(Forces)
These activities develop the idea from the previous page that moving air can cause objects to move. Encourage children to try moving things by blowing. You can also try blowing through a straw.

**12  Day and night**
(The Earth in space)
The comparison between night and day comes up in many parts of the National Curriculum. When talking about the sky, discuss how the aeroplanes and the birds are quite close to the Earth while the stars and moon are very far away.

**13  Light**
(Light)
The picture is designed to prompt discussion about the numerous sources of light around us. Most of our light comes from electricity. Flames can provide some light. Our greatest source of light is the sun.

**14  Countryside sounds**
(Sound and music)
There is lots of detail in this picture, and plenty of examples of sound.

# 1 Odd one out

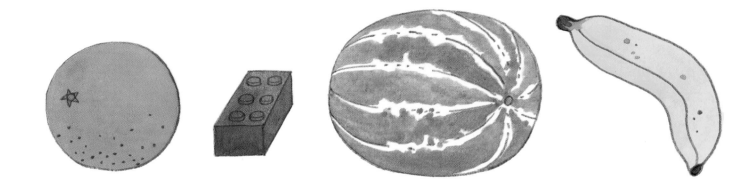

Which one can't you eat?

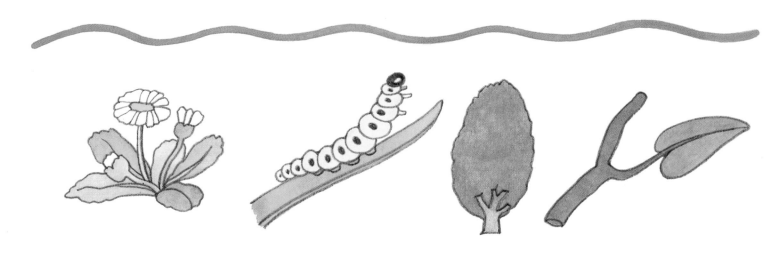

Which one can walk?

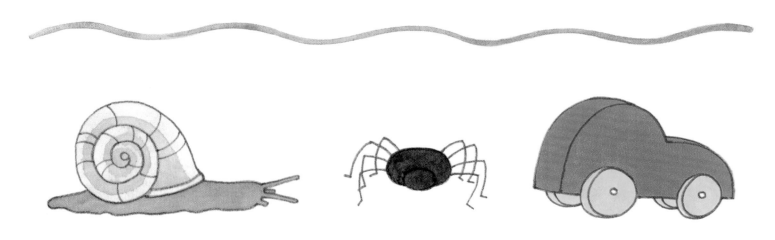

Which one isn't alive?

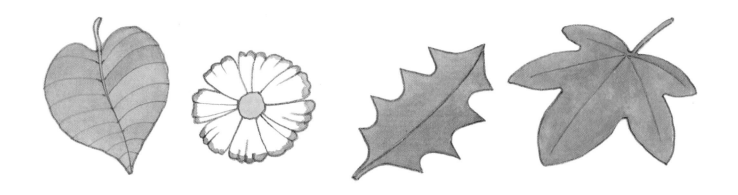

Which one isn't a leaf?

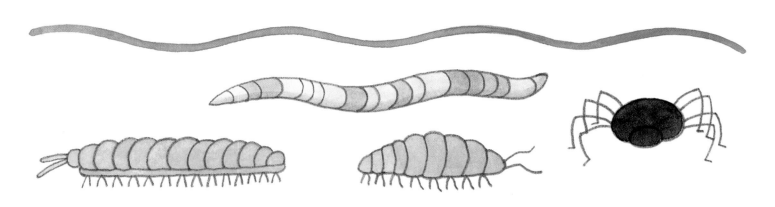

Which one doesn't have legs?

Which one can't see?

# 2 Living things

Living things are things which grow.
Which of these things do you think are alive?
If you look around, what can you see that is alive?

Which of these things do you think
are animals? Which are plants?
What other plants and animals
can you think of?

# 3 Where flowers grow

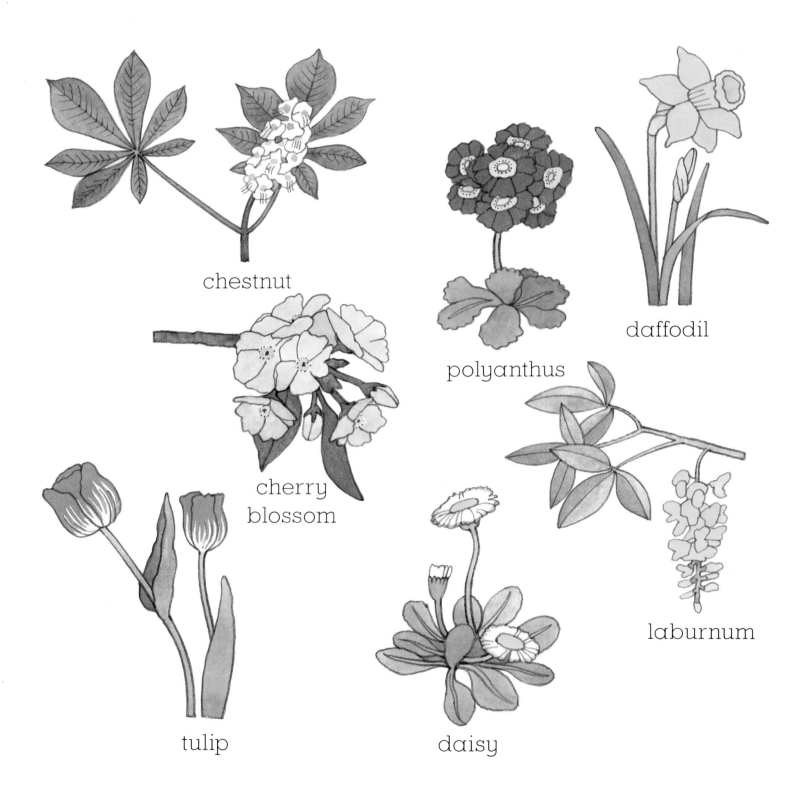

chestnut

polyanthus

daffodil

cherry
blossom

laburnum

tulip

daisy

Look at the flowers above.
Many plants need flowers to produce seeds.

Match the flowers on the left with the plants in
the picture.
Some flowers are on small plants near the ground;
some grow on trees.

# 4   From bud to seed

On this dandelion plant, find a bud that is beginning to open.

What colour flower does it turn into?

How do you think the seeds are spread?

What do you think happens next?

Winter

Spring

Summer

Autumn

Here are some fruits growing on a tree.
When do the flowers appear?
When can you see the apples first appearing?
When are the apples ripe for picking?

# 5 Different kinds of fruit

Fruits are all different colours and shapes.
Which ones are hard?
Which ones are juicy?
Which ones do you usually peel?

Many fruits contain seeds. All pips are seeds.
Find the seeds or pips in the pictures.
Have you ever tried planting seeds?

# 6 Natural collections

These are things you might find in the park.
How many kinds of leaves are there?
How many kinds of nuts and fruits?
Has there been a bird in the park?

Guess where you might find all the things on this page.

Which do you think have come from animals?

# 7  Litter collection

All these things were dropped one day in the street.
Which would you have put in a litter bin?

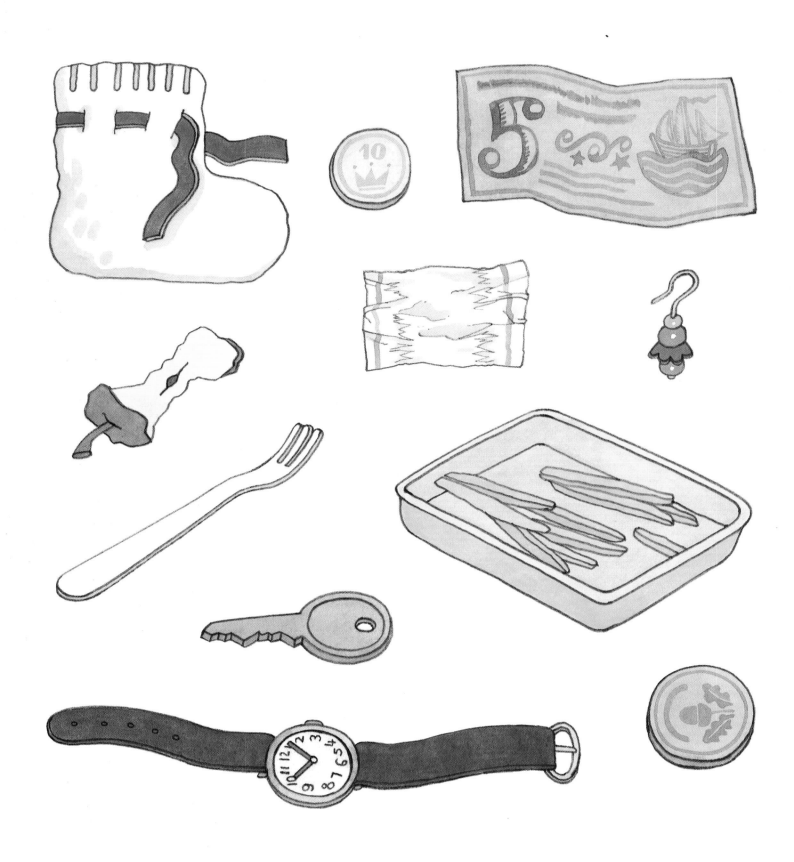

Which things could have been used again?
Which things might people miss?

# 8 Hard and soft

Which things on these pages would you
expect to be hard?
Touch some of the things around you now.
Which feel hard?

Which things on these pages do you think
would feel soft?
Which objects near you now
feel soft and squashy?

# 9 Materials

Each group has a metal, a plastic and a
wooden object.
Which is which?

What do you think these things are made of?
Look around your house and guess what things
are made of.

# 10 Windy day

Look at the picture.
Which way is the wind blowing?
How can you tell?

Which of the objects in the picture are being
moved by the wind?
Which things will only work when the wind
is blowing?

# 11 Moving air

Air can be used to make things move. These three children are using air in different ways to make the paper move. Which has made it move furthest? Try it yourself. Do you get the same result?

Which of these objects are harder to move
by blowing?
Try them and see.

# 12 Day and night

What differences can you see between daytime
and night-time?

Now look at the sky in the two pictures.
What different things can you see?

# 13  Light

Which things in this picture can give out light?

What can give out light in your room now?

# 14  Countryside sounds

What in the picture makes a noise?
Can you make some of the sounds?

Now sit very still and listen.
What sounds can you hear around you?
Are they near or far away?

First published 1990 by Walker Books Ltd
87 Vauxhall Walk, London SE11 5HJ

This edition published 2003

10 9 8 7 6 5 4 3 2 1

Text © 1990 Graham Peacock
Illustrations © 1990 Clare Beaton

This book has been typeset in Rockwell Light Educational

Printed in China

British Library Cataloguing in Publication Data:
a catalogue record for this book is available from the British Library

ISBN 1-84428-806-4

www.walkerbooks.co.uk